Feelin[illegible]
About Friends

Grades 3–6

Written by Linda Schwartz
Illustrated by Beverly Armstrong

The Learning Works

Dedicated to Bobbe Dartanner —
a very special friend.

Edited by Sherri M. Butterfield

Contents

Introduction

Everyone needs a friend. Some people need to have a lot of friends around them; others are satisfied to have a few close ones. Sometimes you choose friends; at other times friends choose you. Some people make friends easily; other people are shy and find it more difficult to make friends. Some friendships last for many years; others last for only a short time.

Having friends your own age is important. Although you can share many experiences, feelings, and ideas with your parents, brothers, sisters, grandparents, or other relatives, you usually have more in common with friends your age. These friends tend to look at things the same way you do because they have many of the same fears, interests, opinions, problems, and worries that you have. A best friend can listen and understand how you feel whether you are dealing with a problem at school or at home. A best friend is there when you are feeling down, when you want to talk and need a good listener, or when you want to share a happy experience.

This book will put you more in touch with your feelings. It will help you identify the special qualities that you possess as a person, clarify your values, and decide what characteristics to look for in friends. It will also provide you with constructive steps to take in making friends and in resolving differences—especially when they threaten your friendships.

Name ______________________

What Is a Friend?

What is a friend? Have you ever asked yourself this question? It is not an easy one to answer because the word ***friend*** is hard to define. This word means different things to different people. Instead of trying to *define* this word, it may be easier to *describe* a friend by saying what he or she does or does not do. Below are some brief descriptions of a friend.

A friend is someone who accepts you the way you are.

A friend is someone who needs you.

A friend is someone you can count on, even in bad times.

A friend is someone you can feel close to and can share your feelings with.

A friend is someone you enjoy being with.

Name ____________________

What Is a Friend?
(continued)

In the spaces below, write and illustrate your own answers to the question: What is a friend?

Name ______________________________

All Kinds of Friends

Friends come in all ages and sizes. They can be humans or animals. They can live close by or far away. In the spaces below and on page 8, name and describe a friend who

is your age,

____
(name)

____

____

____

____

is older than you are,

____
(name)

____

____

____

____

is younger than you are,

____
(name)

____

____

____

____

is a member of your family,

____
(name)

____

____

____

____

is *not* a member of your family,

____
(name)

____

____

____

____

Name ______________________

All Kinds of Friends
(continued)

lives close by,

____
(name)

____
____
____
____
____

lives far away,

____
(name)

____
____
____
____
____

is a teacher,

____
(name)

____
____
____
____
____

is an animal or pet,

____
(name)

____
____
____
____
____

does not fall into any of these categories but is important to you.

____
(name)

____
____
____
____

Name ______________________________

Feelings About Friends

Complete each sentence.

1. Friends are important to me because ______________________________

____.

2. I need a friend when ______________________________

____.

3. Friends think that I am ______________________________

____.

4. Friends like me because ______________________________

____.

5. I feel happy when a friend ______________________________

____.

6. I feel unhappy when a friend ______________________________

____.

7. My friend makes me angry when ______________________________

____.

8. When a friend teases me, I usually ______________________________

____.

Name ______________________

Feelings About Friends
(continued)

9. I like being with people who ______________________

____.

10. I would rather *not* waste time with people who ______________________

____.

11. I enjoy talking with my friends about ______________________

____.

12. Some things I enjoy doing with my friends are ______________________

____

____.

13. A quality that I admire in friends is ______________________

____.

14. A special quality that I bring to a friendship is ______________________

____.

15. Something I could do to become a better friend is ______________________

____.

16. Someone I would like to get to know better is ______________________

____.

Name ______________________________

Who Are You?

Friendship really starts with you. You need to become acquainted with yourself and feel good about yourself before you can be a friend to others. How well do you know yourself? Read the list of adjectives below. Put a check mark in the box beside each adjective that could be used to describe you *most* of the time. Making these choices will help you understand yourself.

- ☐ academic
- ☐ active
- ☐ athletic
- ☐ bored
- ☐ critical
- ☐ flexible
- ☐ funny
- ☐ happy
- ☐ healthy
- ☐ honest
- ☐ idealistic
- ☐ impatient
- ☐ insensitive
- ☐ kind
- ☐ lazy
- ☐ lonely
- ☐ loyal
- ☐ messy
- ☐ moody
- ☐ neat
- ☐ optimistic
- ☐ outgoing
- ☐ passive
- ☐ patient
- ☐ pessimistic
- ☐ punctual
- ☐ sad
- ☐ scared
- ☐ sensitive
- ☐ serious
- ☐ shy
- ☐ stubborn
- ☐ sympathetic
- ☐ talkative
- ☐ tardy
- ☐ temperamental
- ☐ tense
- ☐ thoughtful
- ☐ tolerant
- ☐ understanding
- ☐ weepy
- ☐ worried

Name ______________________________

How Do You Rate as a Friend?

To discover what kind of friend you are to others, mark the answers that best describe you.

	Never	Sometimes	Always
1. I keep the promises I make to my friends.	☐	☐	☐
2. I let my friends know how much they mean to me.	☐	☐	☐
3. I am a good listener.	☐	☐	☐
4. I talk over misunderstandings.	☐	☐	☐
5. I apologize when I am wrong.	☐	☐	☐
6. I stick by my friends when they are going through rough periods.	☐	☐	☐
7. I go out of my way to help a friend.	☐	☐	☐
8. I make new students at school feel welcome.	☐	☐	☐
9. I return the things I borrow in good condition.	☐	☐	☐
10. I talk behind my friends' backs.	☐	☐	☐
11. I embarrass my friends in front of others.	☐	☐	☐
12. I must have things my own way.	☐	☐	☐
13. I brag about myself to my friends.	☐	☐	☐
14. I criticize my friends in front of others.	☐	☐	☐
15. I pick on other kids.	☐	☐	☐

Name ______________

Nobody's Perfect

On a separate sheet of paper, write a two-paragraph description of yourself. In the first paragraph, describe your strengths and some of the other qualities you are glad that you possess. In the second paragraph, describe your faults and some of the characteristics that may make you hard to have as a friend.

Do others see you as you see yourself? Ask a friend to write a brief description of you in which he or she mentions both strengths and weaknesses. Compare your friend's description of you with your own. In what ways are they similar? In what ways are they different? Does this friend see you as you see yourself?

Name ______________________

Hints on How to Be a Friend

Be trustworthy.

When a friend tells you a secret, keep it. Don't repeat it to others. Trust is a vital part of friendship. Loss of trust can destroy a friendship.

Be sensitive.

Be aware of a friend's needs. Try to know when your friend needs to be with you and when your friend wants to be alone. Respect his or her wish for privacy and need for personal space.

Be dependable.

If you make a promise to a friend, keep it. Don't let your friend down. Be there for him or her in good times as well as bad. Let friends know they can count on you.

Be a good listener.

Kids like to talk to someone who listens actively. Show a genuine interest in the things that are important to your friend. Maintain eye contact while he or she talks.

Be honest.

Let a friend know how you feel. If a friend says or does something that hurts you, talk it over with him or her privately. Express your feelings as honestly as you can, and encourage your friend to do the same.

Name ____________________

Do You Wear a Mask?

Sometimes, the way you feel about yourself is not what you show to others.

Barbara feels inferior to her friends, but she covers up her feelings by doing exactly what the popular girls in her class do. In this way, she hopes to make everyone think that she is popular, too.

Because Jason wants to be liked and accepted by his peers, he goes along with what his friends suggest and seldom disagrees with them. But many times, Jason is unhappy and doesn't know why.

On the lines below, describe a time when you felt one way but acted as if you felt another way.

____

____

____

____

How might you have handled this situation more openly and honestly?

____

____

____

____

Name ________________________

Characteristics of a Friend

Characteristics are those special qualities of personality and appearance that make one person different from another. Here is a list of some characteristics. Circle the ones you would want your friend to have.

ambition	energy	neatness
attractiveness	enthusiasm	patience
bravery	fairness	politeness
cleanliness	gentleness	popularity
cleverness	happiness	sensitivity
consideration	helpfulness	seriousness
courage	honesty	strength
creativity	intelligence	talent
dependability	kindness	truthfulness
discipline	loyalty	wealth

Which of these characteristics are most important? List ten of them in the order of their importance.

1. ________________________
2. ________________________
3. ________________________
4. ________________________
5. ________________________
6. ________________________
7. ________________________
8. ________________________
9. ________________________
10. ________________________

Name ______________________________

Wish List

Think about some of your friends and friendships. What changes would you want to make in them? Check all of the responses that apply.

- ☐ I wish that I had more friends.
- ☐ I wish that I had different friends.
- ☐ I wish that I could get along better with my friends.
- ☐ I wish that I could get to know my friends better.
- ☐ I wish that I could win back a friend I have lost.
- ☐ I wish that I did not disagree with my friends so often.
- ☐ I wish that my friends would treat me better.
- ☐ I wish that my friends would like me for myself instead of for the things I have and do.
- ☐ I wish that I did not have to brag about myself and my accomplishments to make people like me.
- ☐ I wish that my friends were more sensitive to *my* feelings.
- ☐ I wish that my friends would take a greater interest in *me*.
- ☐ I wish that I could be a leader among my friends.
- ☐ I wish that I did not have to be the one who always makes the decisions when I am with my friends.

In looking over my wish list, I see that I ______________________________

____

____.

One thing concerning friends which I am going to try to change is ________

____.

Name ______________________

How Well Do You Know Your Best Friend?

Take this quiz to discover how well you know your best friend.

My best friend's

name is ______________________.

nickname is ______________________.

age is ______________________.

birthday is ______________________.

birthplace is ______________________.

My best friend's favorite

food is ______________________.

hobby or interest is ______________________.

sport or game is ______________________.

type of book is ______________________.

kind of music is ______________________.

movie is ______________________.

subject in school is ______________________.

television program is ______________________.

My best friend.

likes to ______________________.

is afraid of ______________________.

gets mad when ______________________.

would like to change his or her ______________________.

worries about ______________________.

is happy when ______________________.

Discuss your answers with your best friend to see how accurate they are.

Name ______________________

Remember When . . .

Think about a time when you were there to help a friend who really needed you. What happened? How did you help? How did helping make you feel? Write about this time on the lines below.

Name ______________________

Think and Write

Read each question, think about it, and then write a response to it.

What do you look for in a friendship?

____

____

____

____

____

____

____

____

What is there about you that makes people want to be your friend?

____

____

____

____

____

____

____

____

Name ______________________

Think and Write
(continued)

How did you make a new friend in the past?

____
____
____
____
____
____
____
____

What do you and your best friend have in common? In what ways are you alike? In what ways are you different?

____
____
____
____
____
____
____
____

Name ______________________

Tips on Making Friends

While you probably have a few close friends already, you may wish to make some new ones. Below and on page 23 are some tips on making friends.

Look inward.

Examine yourself.
What kind of friend are you?
What kind of person would you like to have as a friend?
Do you know someone who needs your friendship?

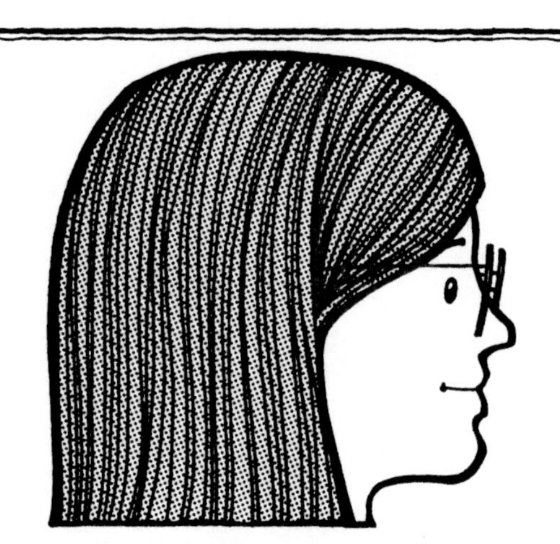

Be yourself.

You want people to like you the way you are. Don't put on an act or pretend to be something you aren't. Instead, be natural, honest, and sincere.

Be considerate.

Consider the other person's interests when you are making plans and the other person's feelings when you are talking or listening.

Name ________________________________

Tips on Making Friends
(continued)

Be diplomatic.

Express your opinions carefully. Don't confront, criticize, or make unflattering comparisons.

Get involved.

Try something new.
Don't let fear of failure keep you from signing up for a new activity or accepting a new responsibility.
Sign up for a class or try out for a part in a play.
Join a band, chorus, club, or team.
In groups of this kind, each person is an important part of the whole.
Group members depend on one another. In time, this mutual trust produces lasting friendships.

Reach out.

Often it is easier to get to know someone on a one-to-one basis than it is in a group. Pick a person you would like to know better. Invite this person to spend time with you doing something you would both enjoy, such as watching a movie, playing a game, or just taking a walk. Find time to talk. When you do so, ask about likes and dislikes, interests and experiences. The way to build a friendship is to share feelings, ideas, and experiences.

Name ____________________

Manipulating

The English word **manipulate** means "to control by unfair means to gain one's own advantage." Some kids manipulate their friends to get their own way. They do so in one of these ways.

being bossy

whining and complaining

making them feel guilty

threatening not to like them anymore or to find another "best friend"

1. Write about a time when a friend manipulated you to get his or her own way.

____

____

____

2. Describe a time when you manipulated a friend to get your own way.

____

____

____

The next time you are trying to persuade a friend to agree with you, instead of using manipulation, be direct. Ask for what you want and explain your reasons for wanting it. Then be willing to discuss it.

Name ______________________

Dealing with Bullies

A **bully** is someone who is often threatening or cruel to those who are smaller or weaker.

Dave is self-conscious about being one of the shortest boys in his class. To make himself feel better, he picks on younger kids and bosses them around.

Jeff's dad is always yelling at him and criticizing the things he does. Because Jeff feels angry and unloved, he picks fights with smaller boys at school.

Nancy is unsure of herself and doesn't feel liked by others. To impress her classmates, she makes fun of other girls.

There are several ways to deal with people who bully you.

1. **Ignore them.** Sometimes, just ignoring name-calling or teasing makes a bully stop. If you don't get upset, the bully receives no pleasure from teasing you and may decide to leave you alone.
2. **Confront them.** Sometimes, asking bullies the reasons for their behavior makes them realize what they are doing and decide to stop.
3. **Include them.** Sometimes, inviting a bully to join your group or team makes the bully feel included rather than left out and causes him or her to act less hostile or resentful.
4. **Talk it over with others.** Sometimes, nothing works. If you can't handle the situation, ask a parent, teacher, or friend for help.

Name ______________________

The Ups and Downs of Friendship

Friendships have their ups and downs. Even best friends sometimes have misunderstandings and disagree. When things do not go smoothly between you and a close friend, it does not mean that your friendship is over. It simply means that you both need to talk things over and to express your feelings.

On the lines below, write about a time when you and a close friend had a serious disagreement. Tell what you disagreed about and how you resolved your disagreement.

____

____

____

____

____

____

____

____

____

____

Name ______________________________

Advice Galore

Pretend that you write a popular advice column for a newspaper. Respond to the problems described in the letters below and on pages 28 and 29.

Dear ______________________________,
(your name)

When my friend Steve and I get together, it seems that we always end up doing what he wants to do and never do what I want to do. How can I get Steve to do what I want?

Steve's Friend But Not His Slave

Dear Steve's Friend,

____

____

____

____

____

Dear ______________________________,
(your name)

I have a good friend named Ann. We have fun together, but she acts hurt when I ask someone else to sit with us at lunch. Although I like Ann very much, I don't enjoy being alone with her all of the time. What should I do?

Puzzled in Pennsylvania

Dear Puzzled,

____

____

____

____

____

Name ______________________________

Advice Galore
(continued)

Dear ______________________________,
(your name)

My friend Linda is good at math. She brags about her math grades all the time. Math is my worst subject. When I ask Linda for help with an assignment, she belittles me and makes me feel dumb. How can I get her to realize that no one is smart in everything?

Mixed-up Mathematician

Dear Mixed-up,

____

____

____

____

____

Dear ______________________________,
(your name)

Matt and I get along well when it's just the two of us; but as soon as someone else joins us, it never works out. Matt and the other guy always take sides against me, and that hurts. What should I do when this happens?

Hurt in Helena

Dear Hurt,

____

____

____

____

____

Name ________________________

Advice Galore
(continued)

Dear ______________________,
(your name)

My friend Douglas doesn't always tell the truth. Sometimes he stretches the truth, and other times he tells lies just to get attention. As a result, I don't know when to believe him and when not to. I don't want to hurt his feelings, but this bad habit of his is ruining our friendship. What can I do?

Perplexed in Pittsburgh

Dear Perplexed,

____

____

____

____

____

Dear ______________________,
(your name)

Maria is my best friend. A few days ago, I told her some very personal things. I asked her not to tell anyone else, and she promised me that she wouldn't. I just found out that she shared everything I told her with two other girls at school. I am so mad at her! How shall I handle this?

Angry Annette

Dear Angry,

____

____

____

____

____

Name ______________________

A Friendly Gesture

Do something nice for a friend. Follow one of these suggestions or create a friendly gesture of your own.

Make and send a greeting card to your friend.

Pay your friend a sincere compliment.

Make a treat for your friend's lunch.

Invite your friend to do something fun with you.

Share your favorite book with a friend.

Write a letter to a friend who lives out of town.

Help your friend with a school assignment.

Teach your friend to play a game that you know well.

Call your friend on the telephone just to say, "Hi!"

Name ______________________

Send a Friend-O-Gram

Send a Friend-O-Gram. Fill out the form below, decorate it, cut it out, and mail it to a friend, thanking him or her for a special friendship.

Friend-O-Gram

DATE	TIME SENT
	A.M. / P.M.

FRIEND'S NAME ______________________

STREET ADDRESS ______________________

CITY, STATE, AND ZIP CODE ______________________

MESSAGE ______________________

____

____

____

____

____

____

____

SENDER'S NAME	SENDER'S TELEPHONE NUMBER

Name ___________________

Friendship Awards and Coupons

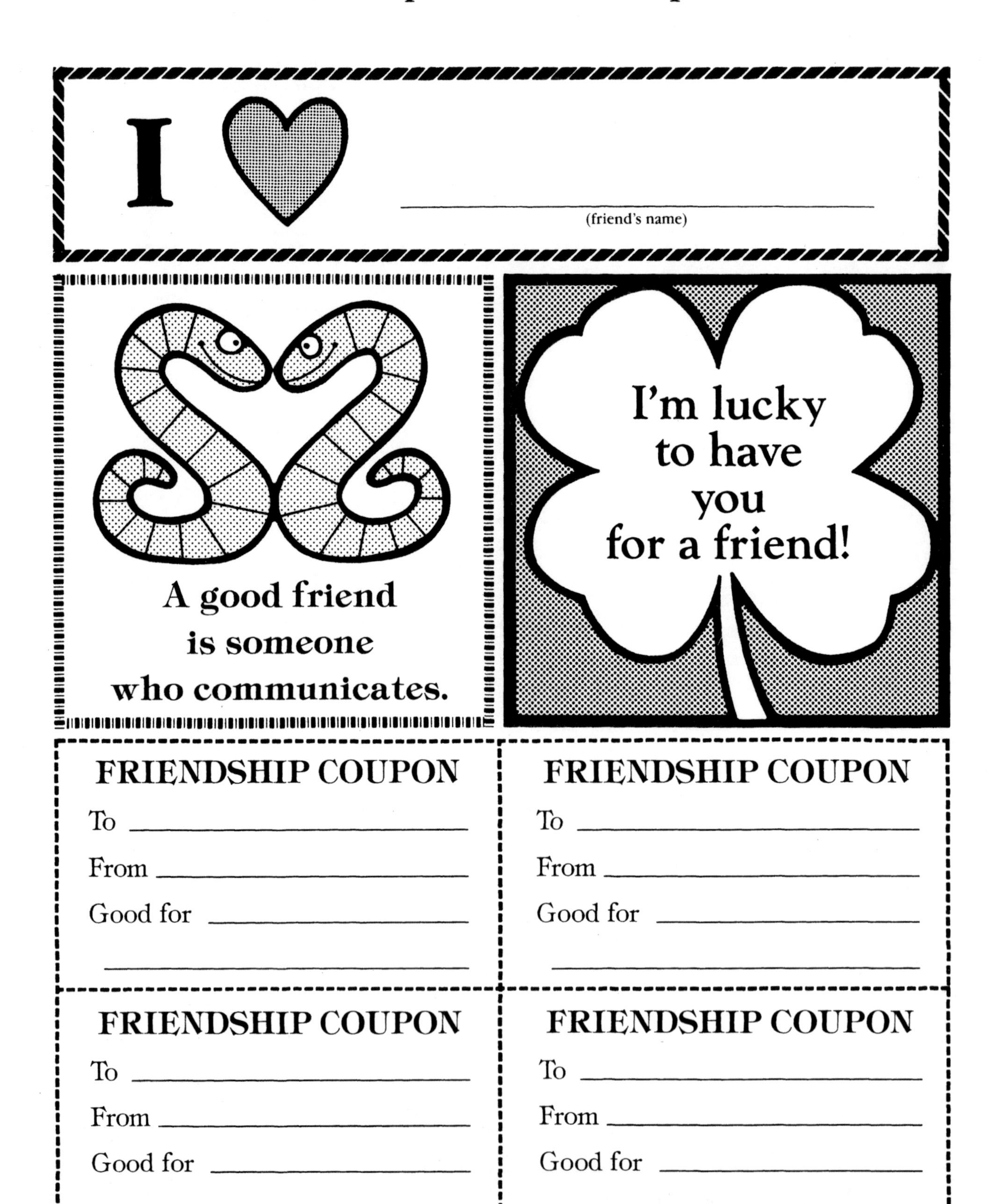